THIS BOOK BELONGS TO:

S0-ALI-427

TOP SECRET
CONFIDENTIAL
CONFIDENTIAL

The Five Mile Press

CONTENTS

Check off each page as you fill it out or memorize its spy-filled information—study fast to become a super sleuth as quickly as possible!

BASIC DETAILS

I want to be a:

❑ Private Investigator
❑ Secret Spy
❑ Detective
❑ Government Agent

My best sleuthing skill is:

I work best:
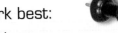
❑ Solo
❑ With a team
❑ By the seat of
my pants!

The life of a spy is:
❑ Exciting
❑ Fast-paced
❑ Unpredictable
❑ Interesting
❑ Dangerous

DAILY TRAINING

Every spy-to-be must have some solid education under their belt—you never know what you will learn to use in your future career!

My school is called:

My favorite subject is:

The worst subject is:

My dream subject would be:

My favorite teacher is:

The best thing about school is:

SPY IN TRAINING

MY SECRET AGENT FRIENDS

Friends (or mission colleagues) are a vital part of successful missions.

My best friends are:

Our favorite things to do when we hang out are:

1.

2.

I first met them at:

STICK
PHOTO
HERE

This is a pic of me and my best buddies:

REMEMBERING THE DETAILS

POW

A spy has an eye for detail and an exceptional memory. Use this space to remember one of the best things you and your friends have done together. Think hard to remember all the little details!

CRAZY CODENAMES

Every spy has a codename to AVOID exposure. The best codename is connected to the user to help identi them to their fellow spies. Use this page to figure out your best codename! Fill in the following to give you some basics to build your codename on.

Favorite sport:

Favorite color:

Favorite celebrity:

Favorite animal:

Favorite hobby:

Other words that describe you:

FOR EXAMPLE:
My favorite hobby is sketching caricatures and I have chosen the following codename based on this:
The friendly cartoonist!

KEEP TRACK OF YOUR CODENAMES

Different missions require different codenames. Keep track of all your aliases right here!

Mission Details	Codename

ID BADGES

MAKE IT PERSONAL
SO IT CAN IDENTIFY
YOU TO THOSE
WHO KNOW YOU!

Create your own Super
Secret Agent ID badge here!

My Secret Agent Badge

Use these shapes to try
out your designs.

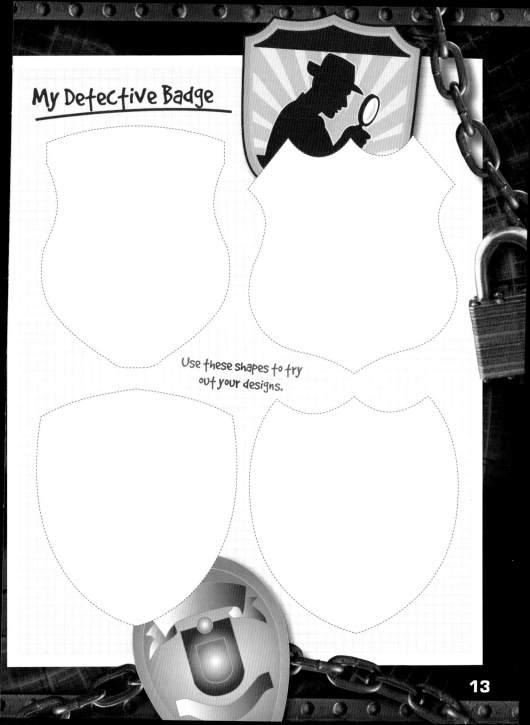

My Detective Badge

Use these shapes to try
out your designs.

MY LIFE AS A SPY

Creative writing opens up your imagination and lets it roam free! Use these pages to write a story about an exciting day in your super secret spy life. What obstacles and dangers will you overcome?

TRAVELING SPY

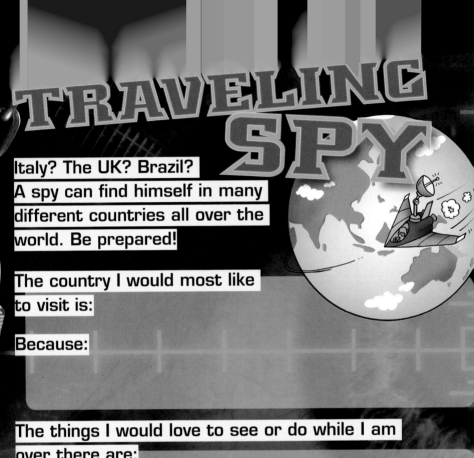

Italy? The UK? Brazil? A spy can find himself in many different countries all over the world. Be prepared!

The country I would most like to visit is:

Because:

The things I would love to see or do while I am over there are:

1. _____
2. _____
3. _____
4. _____

Do they speak another language there? Yes ❑ No ❑
If yes, what language do they speak?

CREATE A TRAVELING SPY KIT

Use this space to record the vital things you will need in your traveling spy kit. Here are a couple of items to get you started!

Pen/pencil
Notepad

Be prepared! What are the top 3 things you need with you at all times?

1.

2.

3.

MY TOP SECRET

The secret service has nothing on your skills!
Brag about all your top talents here—from
the unusual to the quirky ...

MY TOP 3 SKILLS:

1.

2.

3.

MY MOST USEFUL TALENTS:

1.

2.

3.

AGENT TALENTS

MY TOP SLEUTHING SKILLS:

1.

2.

3.

MY WEIRDEST TALENTS:

1.

2.

3.

THE LANGUAGE

Spies travel all over the world—and often they have to blend in with the locals. Be prepared for missions like this by learning some of the local lingo!

Can you speak another language?

_____

FOREIGN DICTIONARY

ENGLISH	FRENCH	GERMAN	ITALIAN
Hello	bonjour	hallo	ciao
Do you …	faites-vous	tun Sie	faccialo
Can I …	peut I	kann ich	può la i
Where	là où	wo	dove
My name is …	mon nom est	mein Name ist	il mio nome è
Goodbye	au revoir	Auf Wiedersehen	arrivederci

OF SPIES

LANGUAGE MISSION

Can you find out more words you would need as a spy?

Language: _____
English word: _____
Foreign word: _____

Language: _____
English word: _____
Foreign word: _____

Language: _____
English word: _____
Foreign word: _____

Language: _____
English word: _____
Foreign word: _____

SPANISH

hola

hágale

puede i

donde

mi nombre es

adiós

THE BEST DISGUISES

QUICK DISGUISES

When you're on stakeout you may need a quick, on-the-spot disguise. If you don't have a cap or sunglasses handy, try to change your posture or walk to avoid getting recognized. It's amazing how distinctive people look when they're just standing!

DEEP COVER DISGUISES

Basically, deep cover disguises are like taking on another persona! So they need to be organized before heading out on your clue-gathering missions. Try using wigs, fake moustaches, glasses …

BLENDING IN

Take note of your surroundings when creating your disguise. For instance, if you want to blend into the environment in your backyard, it's not a good idea to wear bright colors.

DISGUISE DECODER

Stick a photo of yourself here in your best disguise and write a brief about the changes you made.

SUPER STAKEOUT

...ssions are all about gathering clues, which can take
...ong time! Be prepared for some lengthy stakeouts
...our duty to uncover all the pertinent clues ...

...acks! If you are settling in
...a while, make sure you're
...l stocked with food to
...id hunger.

...s, sunglasses, and
...ts are sure disguises
...pinch.

..., paper, and a camera are
...l for recording clues spotted
...our stakeout.

MISSION #1

Set up a stakeout somewhere in your house.
Record the comings and goings of your family
on the next page to hone your surveillance skills.
Don't let any of them spot you!

LEVEL 1
SECURITY
CLEARANCE

**Record the details of
your stakeout here.**

DATE:_____

LOCATION:_____

OBSERVATIONS:_____

_____

_____

_____

_____

_____

_____

_____

_____

_____

_____

_____

CONFIDENTIAL
TOP SECRET
CONFIDENTIAL

ACTIVE SURVEILLANCE

Sometimes a stakeout is not possible and you find you may have to physically follow your target as they move around on their business.

Practice your memory exercises beforehand. You won't have time to write down the clues you spot while you're following your target—you'll have to remember them all until you are finished.

DON'T BE SEEN! Once your target has spotted you your cover is blown. Wear clothes that help you blend into the background. And follow far back enough so that your target doesn't spot you, but not too far away to lose sight of them.

MISSION #2

Set up surveillance on one of your parents!
Track them as they go through their day around
the house, but make sure they don't see you.
Put your memory to the test and write down
your observations on the next page.

Record the details of your surveillance here.

DATE:_____

TARGET:_____

LOCATION/S:_____

_____

_____

OBSERVATIONS:_____

_____

_____

_____

_____

_____

_____

_____

FOR YOUR

27

DETECTIVE
SCHOOL

Everyone should have the chance to go to Detective School!

If I were studying to be a detective my favorite subject would be: (Rank them in order of preference!)

- [ ] Surveillance
- [ ] Code cracking
- [ ] Making disguises
- [ ] Martial arts
- [ ] Foreign language skills
- [ ] Connecting clues
- [ ] Communications
- [ ] Body language

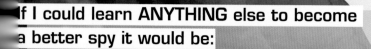

If I could learn ANYTHING else to become a better spy it would be:

The following contacts would make great spy-friends:

SPY RULES

Observe others but remain hidden.

Always be prepared with your super spy kit (see page 38)

Practice your memory and observation skills at every opportunity so you are always prepared.

Stay in shape to jump into immediate action.

Blend into your surroundings.

Keep all your secrets safe from prying eyes!

Trust your instincts!

29

COLLECTING EVIDENCE

Evidence is everywhere and once you know how to find it, uncovering mysterious things will be easy!

FINGERPRINTS: Fingerprints are left everywhere—on glasses, doors, handles, mirrors. When you find them keep them in your book of clues for reference later. Use a piece of adhesive tape to lift a fingerprint off a flat surface. If it is not very clear you can dust a small amount of chalk powder over the top to make it more visible.

PIECES OF PAPER: People leave notes full of random clues lying around all over the place. It could be a meeting time or the location of something special. You never know! If you lightly sketch over a blank piece of paper in a pad, it might reveal an imprint of a message written on the paper that had been on top of it.

SNEAKY TALKING: People let small things slip during a casual conversation. Ask your questions in a round about way to see if you can gather the information you need.

LEVEL 1
SECURITY
CLEARANCE

YOUR EVIDENCE LOG

Choose a location and find yourself some clues. What do these clues tell you?

TOP SECRET

CLUE **1**:_____

_____

_____

_____

CLUE **2**:_____

_____

_____

_____

CLUE **3**:_____

_____

_____

_____

EVIDENCE IDENTIFICATION

Case No.

Date
Time

Test For: ☐ TOXICOLOGY   ☐ FIREARMS
          ☐ DRUGS   ☐ FINGERPRINTS
          ☐ FIBRES/HAIRS   ☐ QUESTIONED DOCUMENTS

Description of Evidence
Location Collected
Crime   Officer   Badge No.

There are times when you'll need to leave a secret trail for your sleuthing friends—and they'll need to know how to follow your covert instructions!

Who is on your secret trail team?

1.

2.

PRACTICE LAYING YOUR TRAIL!

Draw a map of your backyard. On the back of the map write your instructions—in code! (If you need help creating the code have a look on page 40)

If you want to be even more covert, only draw a few of the landmarks you'll need on your map. You'll rely on the familiarity of your friends to fill in the blanks.

Make sure you leave a prize for the first person to decode your map!

SECRET TRAIL

MAP MADNESS

Draw your map here, and then photocopy it to hand out to your friends!

MORSE CODE

If you want to communicate to your spy colleagues in the dark, get a flashlight and use Morse Code! Keep the messages short and simple and you'll be able to stay in touch under any circumstances.

LEARN THE CODE

A: . -	K: - . -	U: .. -	0: - - - - -
B: - ...	L: . - ..	V: ... -	1: . - - - -
C: - . - .	M: - -	W: . - -	2: .. - - -
D: - ..	N: - .	X: - .. -	3: ... - -
E: .	O: - - -	Y: - . - -	4: .... -
F: .. - .	P: . - - .	Z: - - ..	5: .....
G: - - .	Q: - - . -		6: - ....
H:	R: . - .		7: - - ...
I: ..	S: ...		8: - - - ..
J: . - - -	T: -		9: - - - - .

HOT TIP:
This code relies on combinations of short and long flashes of light to indicate letters of the alphabet.

HOT TIP: You can also write this code by using the dots and the dashes used to portray the short and long flashes of light. Use a single slash to separate letters and double slashes to separate words.

SPY DICTIONARY

Want to learn the lingo? Go no further than this intro to the spy phrase book!

Alias: An assumed name or identity

Bug: A secret listening device

Cipher: A code used by spies

Codename: An alias that protects your real name

Cover story: The plausible story that explains the activities of a spy without laying suspicion on their real motives

Dead drop: A pre-organized location to drop messages for your fellow spies

Deep cover: A mission where the spy assumes a complete new identity as they get the job done

Double agent: A spy who you think is on your side but is actually working for the enemy

Mole: A spy who infiltrates the enemy to gather information

INVISIBLE

spy must never stand out in a crowd—these hot tips ill ensure you become the stealthiest sleuth ever!

Keep your eyes moving when on stakeout. A piercing stare is very obvious!.

Use reflections in windows and doors where you can. If you can track your suspect without even facing them you are unlikely to be spotted.

If you are working in a team, one of you can try to anticipate your suspect's path while the other follows from behind.

If you get spotted, change your disguise before continuing surveillance!

If your target turns a corner, use a mirror to watch them so you avoid detection.

YOUR INVISIBILITY SCORE

Practice your surveillance and stakeouts skills and rank your flair for invisibility here!

QUESTION	YES	NO
Were you spotted by your target?		
Were you spotted more than once?		
Did you remember all the clues you saw?		
Did you successfully track your target around a corner with your mirror?		

If you got "YES" more than three times, you rock!

DETECTIVE TOOLKIT

Make your own detective toolkit so you are always prepared for the important things!

Keep these items in a satchel that you can access at all times:

❑ Pen/pencil (for writing clues and notes)

❑ Notepad (for the clues and notes!)

❑ Adhesive tape (for lifting fingerprints)

❑ String (multipurpose tool!)

❑ Compact mirror (for looking behind you and around corners)

Do you want to add anything else to this uber-important toolkit?

1.

2.

3.

READING BODY LANGUAGE

Another useful tool for the spy toolkit is not something you can pack—it is the skill of reading another person's body language.

DID YOU KNOW THAT ...

Sweating or adjusting clothing can be a sign of anxiety.

Open palms during discussion indicates sincerity.

Someone who crosses their arms may be defensive about something.

Fidgeting or refusing to make eye contact is common when people are lying!

READING A PERSON'S BODY LANGUAGE ACCURATELY MEANS READING A COMBINATION OF SIGNS. THESE ARE JUST STARTERS!

CODE BREAKER

Need a hand creating an amazing code your enemies won't be able to crack? Follow some of the top secret ciphers on these pages!

The beauty of all of these codes is that they can be made as individual as you like. You can use them as given here or take the concept and rearrange it to make it all yours!

NEFARIOUS NUMBERS

Replace the letters of the alphabet with numbers.

A	B	C	D	E	F	G	H	I	J	K	L	M	N	O	P	Q	R	S	T	U	V	W	X	Y	Z
1	2	3	4	5	6	7	8	9	10	11	12	13	14	15	16	17	18	19	20	21	22	23	24	25	26

SECRET SYMBOLS

Use very simple symbols to replace the letters. This code looks just like random drawings!

A	B	C	D	E	F	G	H	I	J	K	L	M	N	O	P	Q	R	S	T	U	V	W	X	Y	Z

SNEAKY REPLACEMENTS

Swap the letters of the alphabet around to confuse everyone.

A	B	C	D	E	F	G	H	I	J	K	L	M	N	O	P	Q	R	S	T	U	V	W	X	Y	Z
a	g	o	p	b	f	h	i	k	l	r	s	t	u	v	q	x	c	d	e	y	w	m	n	z	j

Can you use the correct code to figure out this secret message?

13/5/5/20 - 1/7/5/14/20
14/9/7/8/20-15/23/12-1/20
-14/15/15/14!

ANSWER: Meet agent Night Owl at noon!

SECRET MESSAGES

Use one of the secret codes from pages 40 and 41 to write your own secret notes on this page!

CREATE YOUR OWN CODE HERE!

Make your personalized code here.

A	B	C	D	E	F	G	H	I	J	K	L	M

N	O	P	Q	R	S	T	U	V	W	X	Y	Z

Use it to write a secret message below.

MEMORY TESTS

Sharpen your memory with these spy-training tests.

TEST 1

Can your eagle eye spot all the differences between these two pictures?

FIND THE ANSWERS ON PAGE 63!

TEST 2

Study this image closely, then cover it and answer the questions below.

1. What is on the side table?

2. What is Spy Girl reaching for?

3. What color is the pencil in Spy Boy's pocket?

4. What animal is peeping out of Spy Girl's pocket?

How many questions did you get right? 0 1 2 3 4

TRAIN THE EYE

Test your scene-scanning skills with this handy game below.

RULES

When you are at the park, set yourself some goals and see how many things you can spot in a set time frame. If you are playing with a friend, the person who first spots all of the items wins!

Some things you could be looking for are: birds, blue t-shirts, playing ball ...

ITEM	NUMBER OF VIEWINGS

**Try the game in different surroundings!
How about the beach or your schoolyard?**

Location:

ITEM	NUMBER OF VIEWINGS

Location:

ITEM	NUMBER OF VIEWINGS

TRACKING IN YOUR BACKYARD

Learn the art of tracking in your very own backyard! These skills are not only perfect for the great outdoors, but anywhere tracks and footprints can be left behind.

What are the things you can deduce from a footprint in the dirt?

- The approximate shoe size. Is it an adult or a child's footprint?
- Are there different footprints? This means more than one person has passed by here.
- A perfect print means they were walking slowly, but a rough one indicates running.

MISSION #1

Find a footprint in your backyard and untangle all the clues it gives you!

CLUES

Write down your clues here.

HIDE YOUR OWN TRACKS!

Use a branch with leaves to roughly brush out your tracks. You can't make it too neat otherwise it does not look natural.

If you are planning to hide your tracks in advance, walk backwards! That will send anyone following your tracks in the wrong direction.

Disguise the shape of your footprint by tying twigs to the bottom—you'll disguise your footprints as you are walking.

Did You Know?
A "spoor" is another name for a footprint or track in the dirt.

SPY WORD PUZZLES

Test your sleuthing skills and search out these spy-tastic words! Look up, down, and even backwards!

sleuth
skilled
action
detective
codes
disguise
stealth
wigs
stakeout
mission
gadget
spy
clues
evidence

E	C	N	E	D	I	V	E	A	P	S	I
S	T	E	E	T	H	Q	X	M	E	L	A
E	G	D	E	T	E	C	T	I	V	E	T
S	G	I	W	C	A	Y	P	S	B	U	F
K	N	S	X	O	K	C	I	S	K	T	G
I	R	G	A	D	G	E	T	I	L	H	R
L	G	U	A	E	I	C	Z	O	N	E	C
L	R	I	C	S	E	Y	R	N	L	D	L
E	A	S	T	E	A	L	T	H	L	R	U
D	I	E	I	C	K	S	G	S	N	S	E
A	N	S	O	T	U	O	E	K	A	T	S
H	R	A	N	I	O	A	G	W	T	C	R

FIND THE ANSWERS ON PAGE 63!

50

UNDERCOVER AGENT HIGHLIGHTS

The best thing about being a spy is:

The worst thing about being a spy is:

In my life I can use my spy skills to:

SPY LOG SHORTHAND

On stakeouts and surveillance missions you might not have much time to write your notes. The solution? Learn or create your very own shorthand!

CREATE YOUR OWN SHORTHAND

The first couple have been done for you!

Longhand	Shorthand
with	w/
and	&
male	♂
female	♀

24-HOUR TIME

Spies all around the world use 24-hour time. It avoids any confusion about a.m. or p.m. and is recognized by everyone instantly.

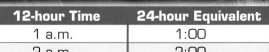

12-hour Time	24-hour Equivalent
1 a.m.	1:00
2 a.m.	2:00
3 a.m.	3:00
4 a.m.	4:00
5 a.m.	5:00
6 a.m.	6:00
7 a.m.	7:00
8 a.m.	8:00
9 a.m.	9:00
10 a.m.	10:00
11 a.m.	11:00
12 p.m	12:00
1 p.m.	13:00
2 p.m.	14:00
3 p.m.	15:00
4 p.m.	16:00
5 p.m.	17:00
6 p.m.	18:00
7 p.m.	19:00
8 p.m.	20:00
9 p.m.	21:00
10 p.m.	22:00
11 p.m.	23:00
12 a.m.	24:00

Did You Know?
24-hour time is expressed in hundreds. For example 21:00 is spoken as "twenty-one hundred hours".

GETTING THE MESSAGE

You have a vital piece of information—how can you get it to your spy-friends or mission partners without getting caught?

DEAD DROP

Organize to drop off the document filled with vital information at a set location. Make it a place your partner can easily pick it up without drawing attention to themselves. The place needs to be concealed so it can't accidentally be picked up by someone else!

BRUSH BY

Walk past your partner without looking at them, but close enough to slyly pass the note between the two of you. Alternatively, as you brush past each other you can drop the scrunched up note in the other's bag.

TOP TIP

Write your note in code so even if your message is intercepted, your information is still safe!

THROUGH

INVISIBLE INK

If your note is intercepted you want to do everything you can to avoid it being read. Even when you write your message in code it shows that there is something someone wants to hide.

To take it one step further you could write your note in invisible ink! This way, even if someone finds the vital information, they won't be able to see it!

HOW TO WRITE WITH INVISIBLE INK:

It's not hard! All you need is the juice of one squeezed lemon ... Use a thin stick or fine paintbrush to write your message and let it dry. Once your partner gets your note they can gently heat the note with a hairdryer or even next to a light bulb to reveal the secrets.

SUSPECT SKETCHING

SUSPECT 1: _____

Seen a suspect and need to describe them to your fellow spies? Practice your sketching skills here. Try sketching someone you are familiar with first, and then try someone new!

SUSPECT 2: _____

CREATE A SECRET

Want to create a language all of your own? You can! Simply start the dictionary of key words here ... Choose some of the most common words you and your friends use and find replacements for them. No one else will know what you guys are talking about!

Original word	Code word
example: treehouse	example: pond

LANGUAGE

Try out your new secret language on this piece of paper.

YOUR SECRET IDENTITY

Don't get your secret identities confused—record them all here!

IDENTITY #1

Identity Name:

Age:

Cover Job:

Background Story:

IDENTITY #2

Identity Name:

Age:

Cover Job:

Background Story:

IDENTITY #3

Identity Name:
Age:
Cover Job:

Background Story:

IDENTITY #4

Identity Name:
Age:
Cover Job:

Background Story:

Super Sleuth Academy

This certificate is to certify that

_____

has graduated from

the Super Sleuth Academy!

Date:

Signature: